Teaching and Learning

Key Stage

Differentiated Activity Book

Letts

EDUCATIONAL

Sentence

Literacy

Year 4

Contents

Introduction

Differentiated Activity Books:

- support the teaching of the Literacy Hour
- help meet the majority of the objectives of the National Literacy Strategy Framework
- contain 30 units of work, sufficient for one school year
- are straightforward and easy to use
- have a clear teaching focus
- contain differentiated activities for each objective at foundation, intermediate and challenging levels of difficulty.

Features of the Sentence Level Teaching Units

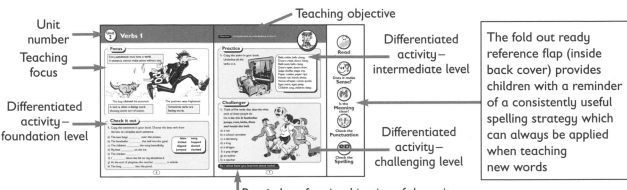

Unit number

Teaching focus

Differentiated activity – foundation level

Teaching objective

Differentiated activity – intermediate level

Differentiated activity – challenging level

The fold out ready reference flap (inside back cover) provides children with a reminder of a consistently useful spelling strategy which can always be applied when teaching new words

Reminder of main objective of the unit

Using the Differentiated Activity Books

A Variety of Uses

The books may be used to:
- introduce and teach individual National Literacy Strategy Framework objectives independently
- introduce individual National Literacy Strategy Framework objectives prior to studying them during Text Level work
- consolidate, develop and extend National Literacy Strategy Framework objectives studied during Text Level work
- provide work for whole class, group or individual work
- provide work for follow-up homework assignments.

Class Work

The Teaching focus provides a clear explanation of each objective with examples for discussion. Appropriate activities may be chosen from the range of differentiated tasks for discussion, or to work through, with the class.

Group and Individual Work

The Differentiated Activity Books are ideal for group and individual work. Work on the same objective may be realistically matched appropriately to individual children's abilities, allowing children to work independently.

Homework

The material in the books provides an ideal solution to meaningful homework assignments that can be differentiated appropriately for each pupil.

Focus

What we write should **make sense** and be **accurate**.

Is it punctuated correctly?

> The boy shouted help. ✗
>
> The boy shouted, "Help!" ✓

Does it make sense?

> The girl got in on the bed. ✗
>
> The girl got in the bed. ✓

Is it accurate?

> She were tired. ✗
>
> She was tired. ✓

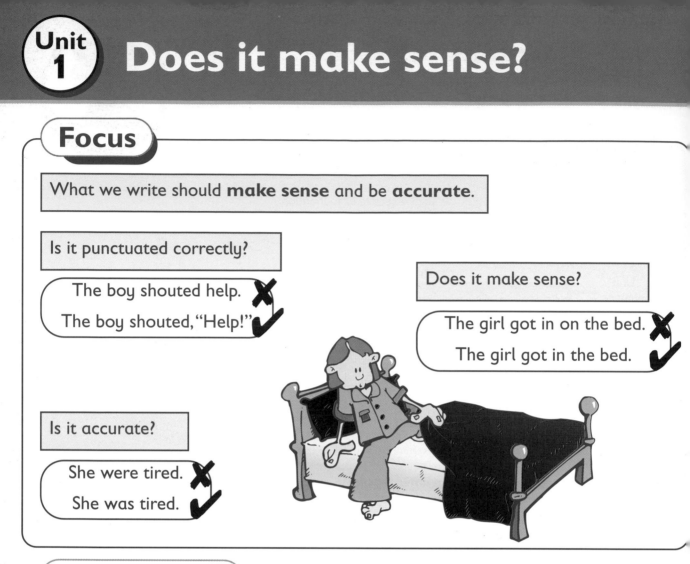

Check it out

1. There is an extra word in each sentence which is not necessary.
Rewrite each sentence in your book, leaving out the word that is not needed.

a) Emma liked to play tricks on and her friends.

b) One day Emma hid under Tom's his bed.

c) He couldn't find her not anywhere.

d) Tom shouted but there was no reply came.

e) Suddenly quickly Tom heard a giggle.

f) Tom realised where Emma she was.

g) He jumped onto on the bed.

h) "Help!" Emma did cried loudly.

i) "You shouldn't not hide under beds," Tom laughed.

Practice

1. Rewrite these sentences in your book and punctuate them correctly. The first one has been done for you.

a) what time is it sam asked ⟶ **"What time is it?" Sam asked.**

b) what a lovely view the mountaineer exclaimed

c) tom has gone to school his sister said to her parents

d) shes not here the girl replied

e) where did i put my glasses the professor asked

f) its just not fair mary shouted you always pick ben

g) hello mrs brown how are you enquired mr jones

h) in his pocket james had a sweet a tissue some gum and a marble

Challenger

1. Rewrite the following sentences correctly in your book.

a) The books what we read was boring.

b) The parcel was returned back to the sender.

c) "I haven't done nothing wrong!" exclaimed the girl.

d) The animal did not take no notice.

e) Give me them apples, please.

f) I seen him go into the shops.

g) The teacher learned them how to swim.

h) She hurted her leg in an accident.

i) A man was at the corner and his dog.

So – what have you learned about checking to make sure sentences make sense?

Unit 2 — Verbs 1

Focus

Every **sentence** must have a **verb**.
A sentence cannot make sense without one.

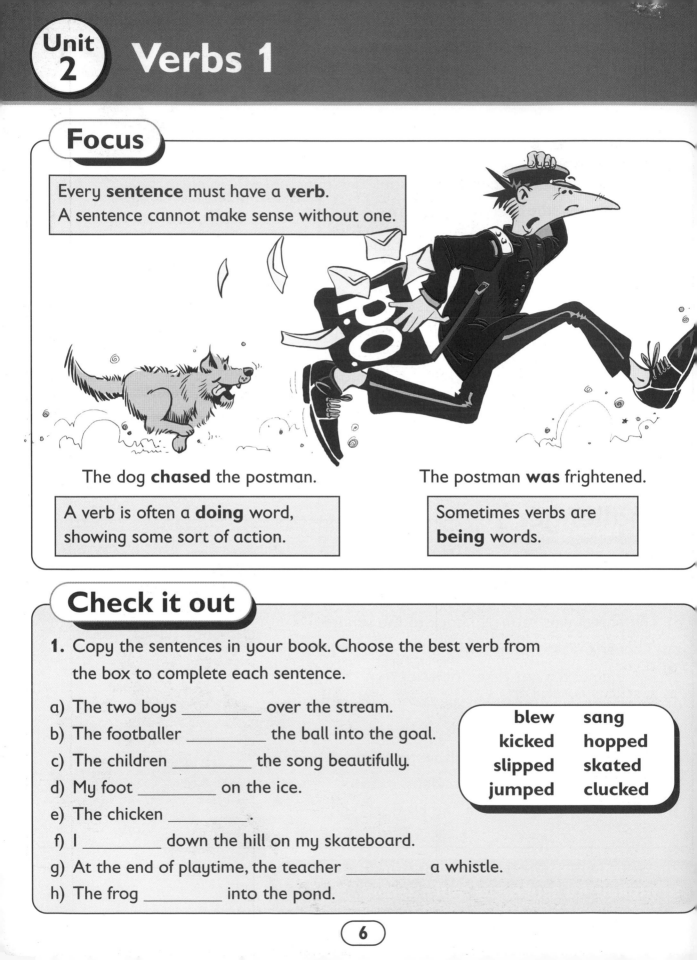

The dog **chased** the postman.

A verb is often a **doing** word, showing some sort of action.

The postman **was** frightened.

Sometimes verbs are **being** words.

Check it out

1. Copy the sentences in your book. Choose the best verb from the box to complete each sentence.

a) The two boys _____ over the stream.
b) The footballer _____ the ball into the goal.
c) The children _____ the song beautifully.
d) My foot _____ on the ice.
e) The chicken _____.
f) I _____ down the hill on my skateboard.
g) At the end of playtime, the teacher _____ a whistle.
h) The frog _____ into the pond.

blew	sang
kicked	hopped
slipped	skated
jumped	clucked

Practice

1. Copy this poem in your book. Underline all the verbs in it.

> Bells tinkle, bells clang,
> Doors creak, doors bang.
> Bells peal, bells clang.
> Doors open, doors slam,
> Steps shuffle, steps trip.
> Paper rustles, paper rips.
> Hands rub, hands shake,
> Voices whisper, voices quake.
> Eyes stare, eyes peep,
> Children sing, children sleep.

Challenger

1. Think of five verbs that describe what each of these do.

   Do it like this: **A footballer jumps, runs, kicks, dives and heads the ball.**

   a) a cat
   b) a school caretaker
   c) a secretary
   d) a frog
   e) a dragon
   f) a pop singer
   g) an author
   h) a teacher

So – what have you learned about verbs?

Focus

The **tense** of the verb tells us **when** the action took place.

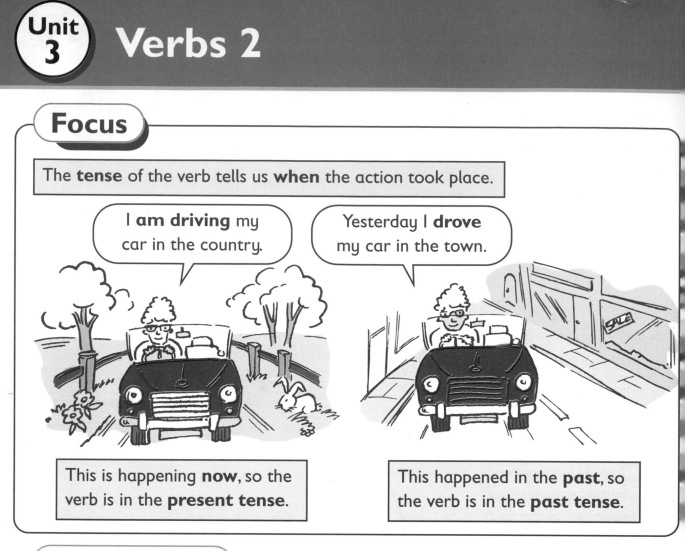

> I **am driving** my car in the country.

> Yesterday I **drove** my car in the town.

This is happening **now**, so the verb is in the **present tense**.

This happened in the **past**, so the verb is in the **past tense**.

Check it out

1. Copy and complete the table below. The first one has been done for you.

Present tense	Past tense
I am playing now.	Yesterday I played.
I am jumping now.	
I am washing now.	
I am shouting now.	
I am laughing now.	
I am working now.	
I am crawling now.	
I am skating now.	

Practice

1. Rewrite these sentences. Change each of the underlined verbs into the past tense. Do it like this:

I <u>cry</u> a lot – I cried a lot.

a) I <u>sing</u> in the bath.

b) I <u>skip</u> with a rope.

c) I <u>pop</u> all the balloons.

d) I <u>carry</u> a heavy bag.

e) I <u>copy</u> all my spellings correctly.

f) I <u>beg</u> to stay up late to watch television.

g) I <u>grab</u> my bag from the kitchen.

h) I <u>supply</u> all my friends with sweets.

Challenger

1. The past tense of the verb in each sentence below is wrong. Rewrite each sentence correctly in your book.

a) I buyed lots of presents at the shops.

b) The boy catched the ball.

c) The man leaved his luggage on the train.

d) The thief stealed a video from the shop.

e) The children drinked their milk quickly.

f) The water on the lake freezed over last night.

g) The ghost shaked his chains to scare the visitors.

h) "Who ringed my bell?" Mrs Ford sayed.

i) The girl weeped quietly at the film.

So – what have you learned about verb tenses?

Focus

> The **tense** of the verb tells us **when** the action took place.
> We use the **present tense** of the verb to tell us what is happening **now.**
> We use the **past tense** of the verb to tell us what happened in the **past**.

A rabbit **lives** in a burrow.
It **eats** grass and plants.

When Rob the rabbit **saw** the owl, he quickly **dived** into his burrow.

> This is taken from an information (a **non-fiction**) text. The verbs are in the **present tense**.

> This is taken from a story (a **fiction** text). The verbs are in the **past tense.**

Check it out

1. Here are some facts about rabbits. Copy the sentences. Underline all the verbs in them like the first one. The verbs are all in the present tense.

a) Rabbits <u>dig</u> a tunnel.

b) This is the rabbits' home.

c) In the daytime, rabbits sleep in their burrows.

d) They stay there until evening.

e) Rabbits have long ears.

f) They run very fast.

g) Lots of rabbits live together.

h) Rabbits have sharp teeth.

i) They eat grass and plants.

Practice

1. Copy this story about a rabbit. Underline all the verbs in it. They are all in the past tense.

> When Rob woke up, he twitched his whiskers and bobbed his tail. He stretched and sniffed the air. Rob felt hungry because it was evening time. Rob walked towards the entrance of the burrow. When he got there, he listened carefully and looked all around. There was no danger so he scampered out. The air was fresh. It was getting dark. Rob nibbled the grass and chewed some dandelions. Suddenly he heard a noise above him. Rob looked up. When Rob saw the owl, he quickly dived into the safety of his burrow.

Challenger

1. Here are the instructions for making a cup of tea – but they are in the wrong order. Copy them out in the correct order. Underline the verbs in each sentence. Are they in the **present** or **past** tense?

> - Stir your cup of tea.
> - Put two teabags into a teapot.
> - Drink your cup of tea.
> - Pour the boiling water into the teapot.
> - Get a cup and pour some milk into it.
> - Pour some water into a kettle.
> - Add some sugar if you like it.
> - Boil the kettle.
> - Pour some tea from the teapot into the cup.

So – what have you learned about using the present and past tenses of verbs?

Focus

The **tense** of the verb tells us **when** the action took place.

We use the **present tense** of the verb to tell us what is happening **now**.
We use the **past tense** of the verb to tell us what happened in the **past**.
We use the **future tense** of the verb to tell us what will happen in the **future**.

Notice that when we write verbs in the future tense, we need a 'helper' verb like **will** to help the main verb.

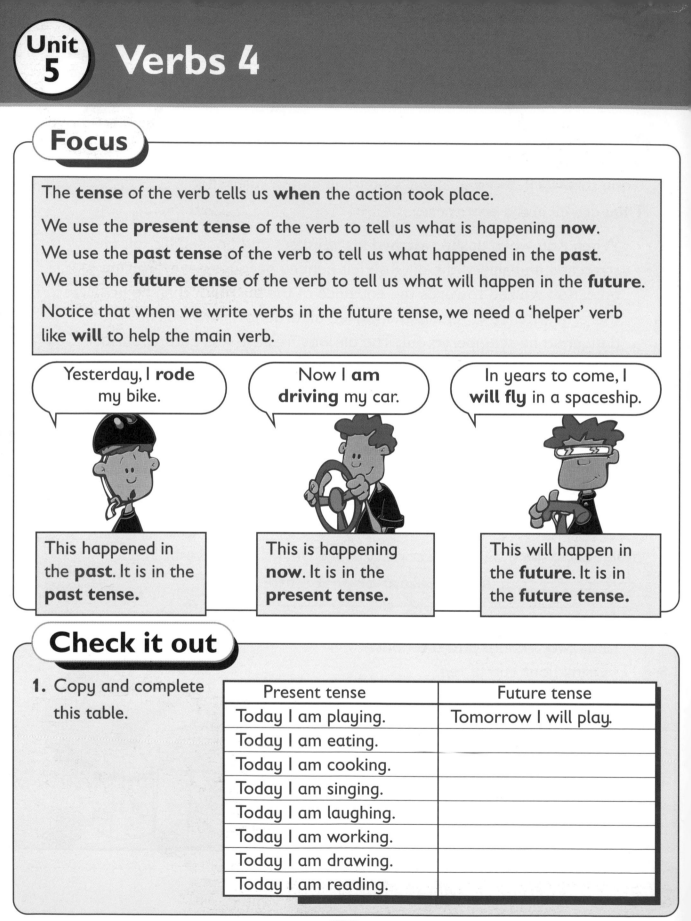

Yesterday, I **rode** my bike.

Now I **am driving** my car.

In years to come, I **will fly** in a spaceship.

This happened in the **past**. It is in the **past tense**.

This is happening **now**. It is in the **present tense**.

This will happen in the **future**. It is in the **future tense**.

Check it out

1. Copy and complete this table.

Present tense	Future tense
Today I am playing.	Tomorrow I will play.
Today I am eating.	
Today I am cooking.	
Today I am singing.	
Today I am laughing.	
Today I am working.	
Today I am drawing.	
Today I am reading.	

Practice

1. Rewrite these sentences. The verbs are all in the present tense.
Change each verb into the future tense. The first has been done for you.

a) I get up early. ⟶ **I will get up early.**

b) I watch television until eight o'clock.

c) I eat cornflakes for my breakfast.

d) I put on my coat and pick up my bag.

e) I go and call for my friend.

f) We walk to school together.

g) We go through the park and play on the swings.

h) We sit next to each other in school.

i) We help each other with our work.

Challenger

1. Here are some questions about the future. Make up some
answers about what you think will happen.

a) Where will you live?

b) What job will you do?

c) What sort of things will you wear?

d) How will people travel?

e) What will people eat?

f) What will your home be like?

g) Where will you go for your holidays?

h) How will robots be used?

i) Will children still have to go to school?

So – what have you learned about the future tense?

Focus

We can sometimes **improve** the sentences we write by **changing the verbs** and making them more **expressive**.

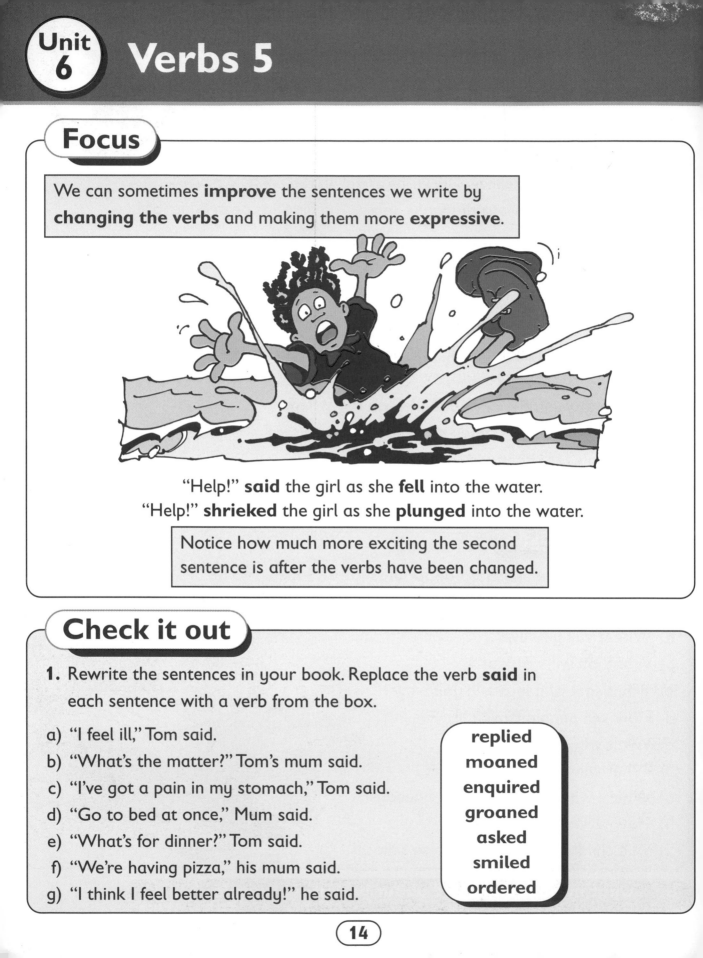

"Help!" **said** the girl as she **fell** into the water.
"Help!" **shrieked** the girl as she **plunged** into the water.

Notice how much more exciting the second sentence is after the verbs have been changed.

Check it out

1. Rewrite the sentences in your book. Replace the verb **said** in each sentence with a verb from the box.

a) "I feel ill," Tom said.

b) "What's the matter?" Tom's mum said.

c) "I've got a pain in my stomach," Tom said.

d) "Go to bed at once," Mum said.

e) "What's for dinner?" Tom said.

f) "We're having pizza," his mum said.

g) "I think I feel better already!" he said.

replied
moaned
enquired
groaned
asked
smiled
ordered

Practice

1. Copy the sentences below. Each time replace the verb **walked** with a more expressive verb.

a) The explorer walked through the dark forest.

b) The soldiers walked across the parade ground.

c) The burglar walked through the house.

d) The weary farmer walked home after a long day.

e) The injured man got up and walked to the side of the road.

f) Captain Bones walked up and down the deck.

g) The toddler walked across the room.

h) The horse walked towards the fence.

i) The hikers walked along the track over the hills.

Challenger

1. Think of another verb which means the same as each of the verbs below. Write a sentence containing each of the alternative verbs you think of. Use a thesaurus to help, if necessary.

a) mix

b) grab

c) pull

d) throw

e) speak

f) argue

g) climb

h) sleep

i) eat

j) draw

k) drink

l) run

So – what have you learned about choosing verbs carefully?

Focus

An **adverb** tells us more about a **verb**.
It **describes** or **modifies the verb** in some way.
Many adverbs end with the suffix **ly**.
Adverbs often tell us **how** something happened.

The captain **proudly** received the cup.

Check it out

1. Copy these sentences in your book. Underline the adverb in each sentence.

a) The lion roared <u>noisily</u>.

b) The man sneezed loudly at the table.

c) I answered all the questions correctly.

d) The little girl smiled sweetly at her grandmother.

e) Shireen gazed longingly at the toys in the shop window.

f) We did the sums easily.

g) The dog growled fiercely at the burglar.

h) I crossed the road carefully.

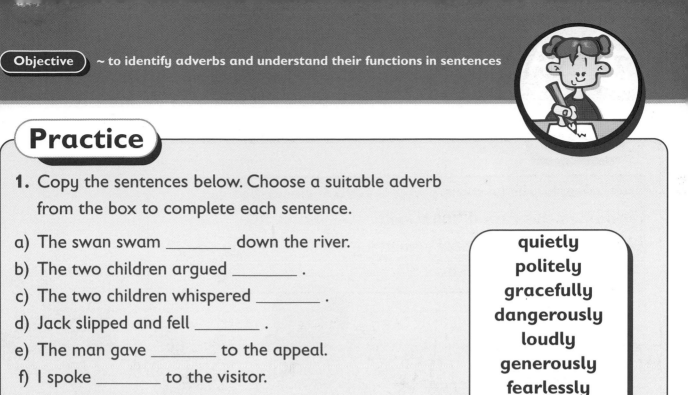

Practice

1. Copy the sentences below. Choose a suitable adverb from the box to complete each sentence.

a) The swan swam _____ down the river.

b) The two children argued _____ .

c) The two children whispered _____ .

d) Jack slipped and fell _____ .

e) The man gave _____ to the appeal.

f) I spoke _____ to the visitor.

g) The girl stood up to the bully _____ .

h) The police stopped the man who drove _____ .

> quietly
> politely
> gracefully
> dangerously
> loudly
> generously
> fearlessly
> awkwardly

Challenger

1. Think of three adverbs which could describe the way you can do things.

Do it like this: **You can eat greedily, noisily, slowly.**

a) You can walk _____, _____, _____.

b) You can laugh _____, _____, _____.

c) You can work _____, _____, _____.

d) You can talk _____, _____, _____.

e) You can read _____, _____, _____.

f) You can run _____, _____, _____.

g) You can sing _____, _____, _____.

h) You can paint _____, _____, _____.

So – what have you learned about adverbs?

Focus

An **adverb** tells us more about a **verb**. It **describes** or **modifies the verb** in some way.

Adverbs often tell us **how** something happened. Many adverbs end with the suffix **ly**.

The winner smiled happily.   The boy cried miserably.   The dog barked loudly.

happy + ly = happily	**miserable + ly = miserably**	**loud + ly = loudly**
If the adjective ends with a consonant **+ y**, we change the **y** to **i** and add **ly**.	If the adjective ends with a consonant **+ e**, we usually drop the **e** and add **ly**.	We can just add **ly** to most adjectives to make an adverb.

Check it out

1. Copy and complete the table. The first one has been done for you.

Adjective	Add **ly** to make an adverb
clever	cleverly
quick	
fair	
sudden	
	willingly
	proudly
careful	
	gratefully

Practice

1. Write the adverb you can make from each of the adjectives below.

a) humble   c) possible   e) idle

b) gentle   d) comfortable   f) simple

2. Write the adverb you can make from each of the adjectives below.

a) hungry   c) lucky   e) pretty

b) noisy   d) weary   f) lazy

3. Write the adjective from which each of these adverbs was made.

    Do it like this: **feebly — feeble**

a) weakly   d) merrily   g) truthfully

b) annually   e) sensibly   h) shabbily

c) steadily   f) nobly   i) truly

Challenger

1. Find the eight adverbs in the puzzle.

    Write some sentences, using each adverb at least once.

q	w	e	w	i	l	l	i	n	g	l	y	s	a	z
k	r	m	r	t	y	h	g	d	f	a	i	r	l	y
h	g	h	u	m	b	l	y	l	k	m	n	b	g	d
q	a	z	x	s	t	e	a	d	i	l	y	c	v	b
a	n	n	u	a	l	l	y	m	n	b	v	c	x	z
l	k	j	h	g	f	h	w	o	e	f	u	l	l	y
w	e	r	t	e	r	r	i	b	l	y	h	g	f	k
s	d	c	x	z	h	e	a	v	i	l	y	m	n	h

So – what have you learned about the way adverbs are formed?

Focus

Our choice of adverbs can affect the meaning of sentences **considerably**.

Amy walked **hurriedly**.   Amy walked **anxiously**.   Amy walked **carefully**.

Check it out

1. Copy the sentences below. Choose a suitable adverb from the box to complete each one.

a) The baby slept _____ .

b) The boy smiled _____ .

c) The children shouted _____ .

d) The girl dressed _____ .

e) The soldier fought _____ .

f) He waited _____ .

g) The car braked _____ .

h) I listened _____ .

bravely
noisily
smartly
patiently
soundly
carefully
happily
suddenly

Practice

1. Rewrite the sentences below. Change the adverb in each sentence to make it mean the opposite.

a) The child took hold of the cat roughly.
b) The girl wrote her story carefully.
c) The people left the room hurriedly.
d) The man spoke indistinctly.
e) I vaguely remembered the visitor's face.
f) The woman landed heavily on the grass when she jumped.
g) The losers accepted defeat sportingly.
h) The boy gave in stubbornly.

Challenger

1. Rewrite the sentences below. Change the adverb in each sentence to alter its meaning.

a) I looked longingly at the new trainers.
b) The thief acted warily when I spotted him.
c) The child eventually decided to dive into the pool.
d) The athlete ran past the finishing line breathlessly.
e) The artist painted the picture beautifully.
f) The cat crept cautiously towards the birds.
g) The motorist was badly injured.
h) The girl frowned angrily when she was told off.

So – what have you learned about the way adverbs can affect the meaning of sentences?

Focus

We can **classify** adverbs according to their **meaning**.
A **thesaurus** is helpful for doing this.

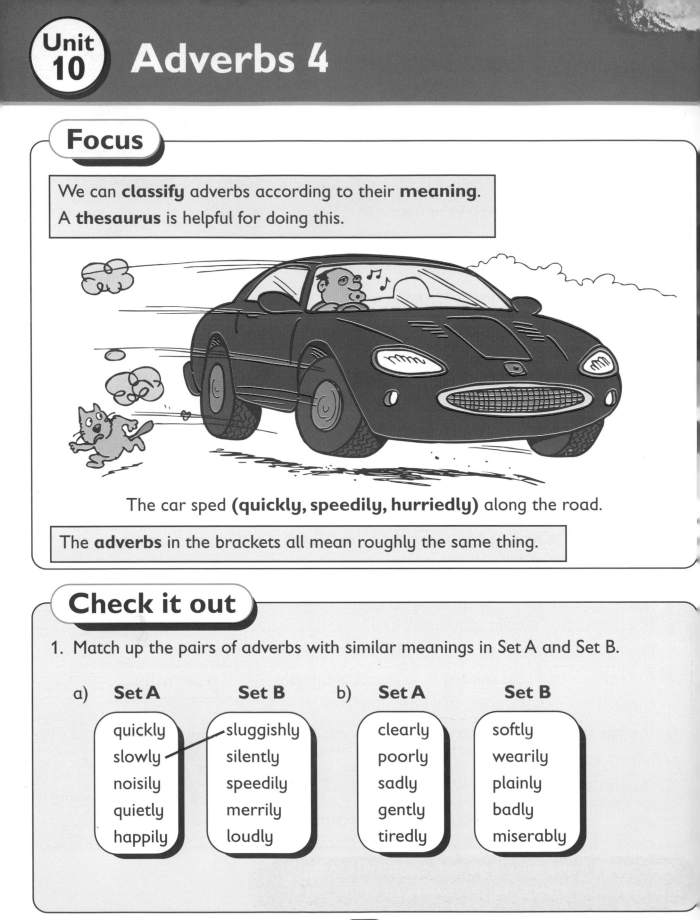

The car sped **(quickly, speedily, hurriedly)** along the road.

The **adverbs** in the brackets all mean roughly the same thing.

Check it out

1. Match up the pairs of adverbs with similar meanings in Set A and Set B.

a)

Set A	Set B
quickly	sluggishly
slowly	silently
noisily	speedily
quietly	merrily
happily	loudly

b)

Set A	Set B
clearly	softly
poorly	wearily
sadly	plainly
gently	badly
tiredly	miserably

Practice

1. Rewrite the sentences below. Replace the adverb in each with an adverb of similar meaning from the box.

a) The man was dressed shabbily.

b) The knight fought the dragon courageously.

c) I will probably try again another time.

d) The shopkeeper eyed the customer warily.

f) I accepted my present gratefully.

g) The children argued furiously.

h) I jumped over the wall awkwardly.

i) The children divided the sweets equally.

> thankfully
> untidily   clumsily
> fairly   angrily
> bravely   possibly
> cautiously

Challenger

1. Divide the adverbs from the word wall into six sets. Each set should contain three adverbs with similar meanings.

pleasantly	expertly	kindly	
	sweetly	cleverly	haughtily
worriedly	abruptly	fearfully	
	tenderly	boastfully	charmingly
anxiously	suddenly	hastily	
	gently	arrogantly	skilfully

So – what have you learned about classifying adverbs according to their meaning?

Focus

Adverbs may be divided into different **types**.

A man was **happily** walking through the woods.

A few minutes **later** he stopped in his tracks.

In front of him **there** stood an enormous bear.

An adverb of **manner** tells us **how** something happened.

An adverb of **time** tells us **when** something happened.

An adverb of **place** tells tells us **where** something happened.

Check it out

1. Copy these sentences in your book. Choose a suitable adverb from the box to fill each gap.

> **Adverbs of manner** – sleepily, slowly
> **Adverbs of time** – later, always
> **Adverbs of place** – here, everywhere

a) My bedroom is _____ in a mess.

b) I was tired so I stretched _____ .

c) I looked _____ for my lost toy.

d) "Come _____ !" the teacher ordered.

e) The car _____ disappeared into the distance.

f) I promised to do my homework _____ .

Practice

1. Copy the table below. Write each adverb in the box in the correct column.

daily	here	happily	near	yesterday
later	lazily	far	angrily	soon
there	slowly	truthfully	now	inside

Adverbs of manner	Adverbs of time	Adverbs of place

Challenger

1. Copy the sentences below. Underline the adverb in each sentence.
   Say if it is an adverb of manner (M), an adverb of time (T) or an adverb of place (P). Do it like this: **Dinner will <u>soon</u> be ready. (T)**

a) Ahead lay the lost city of the Incas.

b) The man slowly walked through the tunnel.

c) I once saw a famous singer.

d) Tom finished the work early.

e) I faced the tiger bravely.

f) The girl won the race easily.

g) The tank was already full.

h) The abominable snowman was nowhere
   to be seen.

So – what have you learned about different types of adverbs?

Focus

Commas tell us to take a **short pause**.
They help you to make sense of what you read.

Have you got your breath back, Tom?

Yes, let's get going again.

After picking up their packs, the two mountaineers set off for the summit.

Commas are used to **separate** any **extra bits** that are added.

Commas help **break up** longer sentences into **smaller parts** to make more sense.

Check it out

1. Rewrite the sentences below. Put in the missing comma in each.

a) Stop that Simone.

b) Have you seen my dog Smudge?

c) Can I stay up late Dad?

d) Look out Omid!

e) Please be quiet Edward.

f) I would like a chocolate a nutty one.

g) Sorry sir.

h) Yes I can do it.

i) I can't manage I'm afraid.

j) We'll go after tea shall we?

Practice

1. Copy the beginnings of each of the sentences below. Write in a suitable ending for each. Don't forget to put in the comma.

a) To my surprise _____.

b) As we walked down the street _____.

c) Even though it was raining _____.

d) After the evening meal _____.

e) Because it was the holidays _____.

f) During the news programme _____.

g) Last of all _____.

h) In the middle of the night _____.

Challenger

1. Copy these sentences. Put in the missing commas.

a) A hedgehog is about 30 centimetres long with prickly spines.

b) Emma picked up her bag glad that school was over.

c) The plane a jet plane sped past in the sky.

d) The lorry was parked in the street near the shops.

e) The darker of the two men the one with the hat was talking.

f) I saw two animals a deer and an elk in the woods.

g) The children who were running were told off by the teacher.

h) The dinosaur a Triceratops lived millions of years ago.

So – what have you learned about using commas?

Focus

Adjectives are describing words.
Adjectives give us more information about nouns.

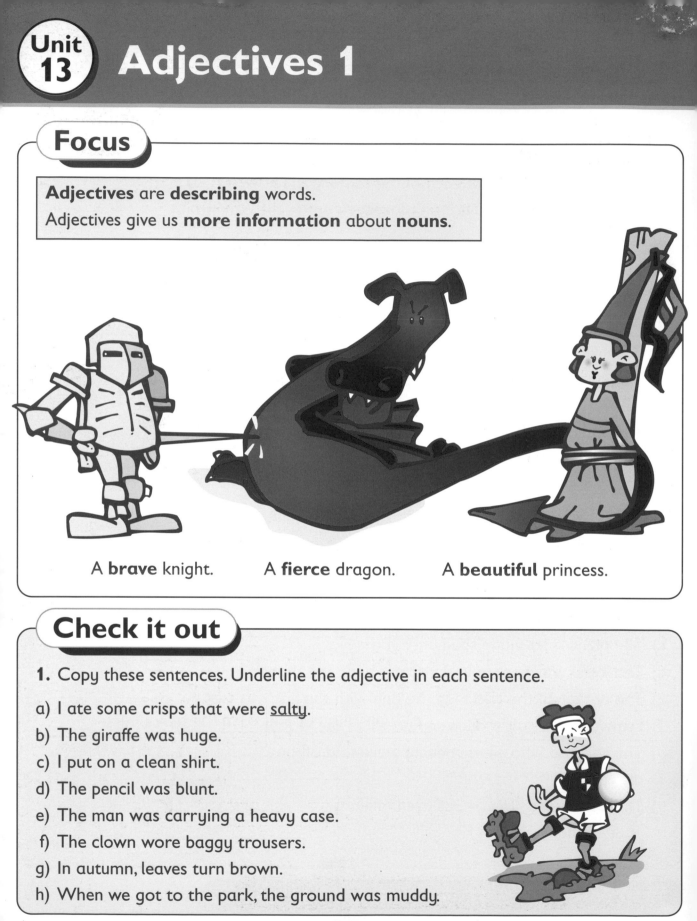

A **brave** knight.   A **fierce** dragon.   A **beautiful** princess.

Check it out

1. Copy these sentences. Underline the adjective in each sentence.

a) I ate some crisps that were <u>salty</u>.

b) The giraffe was huge.

c) I put on a clean shirt.

d) The pencil was blunt.

e) The man was carrying a heavy case.

f) The clown wore baggy trousers.

g) In autumn, leaves turn brown.

h) When we got to the park, the ground was muddy.

Practice

1. A simile compares two things. For example, **as brown as a berry**.
Think of a suitable adjective to complete each of these similes.

a) as _____ as a bee

b) as _____ as a fox

c) as _____ as a lion

d) as _____ as an elephant

e) as _____ as a dove

f) as _____ as a tortoise

g) as _____ as ice

h) as _____ as a feather

i) as _____ as butter

j) as _____ as snow

k) as _____ as honey

l) as _____ as vinegar

Challenger

1. Find eight adjectives in the puzzle. Write a sentence to use each of the adjectives you find.

a	d	g	t	o	u	g	h	n	q	w	u
q	w	b	y	s	t	r	a	i	g	h	t
p	n	a	r	r	o	w	c	d	s	b	n
z	x	g	e	n	t	l	e	m	n	h	v
a	s	i	l	e	n	t	r	y	u	s	k
j	k	h	d	c	a	l	m	l	p	j	a
o	b	r	i	g	h	t	j	n	s	d	g
f	d	i	s	o	b	e	d	i	e	n	t

So – what have you learned about adjectives?

Focus

When we compare two nouns we use a **comparative adjective**.

When we compare more than two nouns we use a **superlative adjective**.

Mr Marvo is **strong**, Mr Samson is **stronger** but Mr Atlas is **strongest** of all.

This is the **root adjective**.

Superlative adjectives often end with the suffix **est**.

Comparative adjectives often end in the the suffix **er**.

Check it out

1. Copy and complete this table.

Root adjective	Comparative form	Superlative form
small	smaller	
light		lightest
	rougher	
green		
		coldest
sour		
	newer	
		smoothest

Practice

1. Write the comparative and superlative forms for each of the adjectives below.
   Do it like this: **large – larger – largest**

   a) wise   c) tame   e) nice   g) cute

   b) safe   d) brave   f) white   h) strange

   Write a sentence to explain what happens to the
   root adjectives when the suffixes are added.

2. Write the comparative and superlative form for each of the adjectives below.
   Do it like this: **busy – busier – busiest**

   a) healthy   c) lucky   e) sturdy   g) empty

   b) noisy   d) pretty   f) heavy   h) tiny

   Write a sentence to explain what happens to the root adjectives when the
   suffixes are added.

Challenger

1. Find the ten comparative and
   superlative adjectives in the
   puzzle. Write them in your book.

2. Now make up some sentences
   using each adjective you found at
   least once.

a	b	c	n	o	i	s	i	e	r	d	e
d	i	r	t	i	e	s	t	h	j	k	n
z	x	c	v	b	w	i	d	e	s	t	v
q	w	e	r	c	o	l	d	e	r	t	y
d	c	l	e	v	e	r	e	s	t	s	x
o	p	j	s	t	r	a	n	g	e	r	p
g	h	s	i	l	l	i	e	s	t	v	c
t	r	y	n	i	c	e	r	b	c	h	u
p	r	e	t	t	i	e	s	t	f	c	x
b	f	h	g	t	r	h	i	g	h	e	r

**So – what have you learned about
comparative and superlative adjectives?**

Focus

We sometimes use an **adverb** in front of an adjective to show **degrees of intensity.**

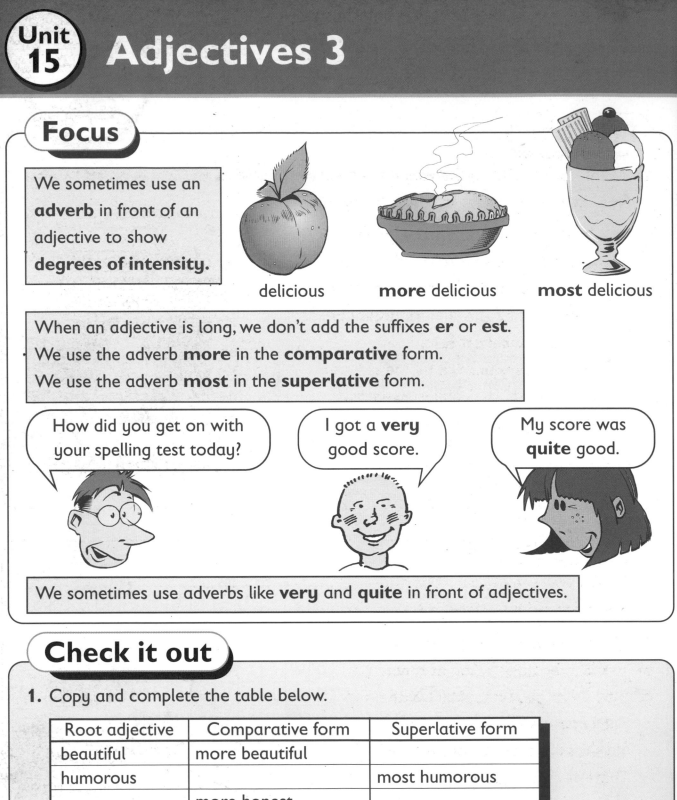

delicious   **more** delicious   **most** delicious

When an adjective is long, we don't add the suffixes **er** or **est**.
We use the adverb **more** in the **comparative** form.
We use the adverb **most** in the **superlative** form.

How did you get on with your spelling test today?

I got a **very** good score.

My score was **quite** good.

We sometimes use adverbs like **very** and **quite** in front of adjectives.

Check it out

1. Copy and complete the table below.

Root adjective	Comparative form	Superlative form
beautiful	more beautiful	
humorous		most humorous
	more honest	
		most efficient
dangerous		
	more comfortable	

Practice

1. There is a mistake in the way each adjective is written in the sentences below. Rewrite the sentences with the correct form.

a) My chair is comfortabler than yours.

b) This is the expensivest shirt I could find.

c) My trainers are more fashionabler than yours.

d) Mr Patel had the most luxuriousest car of all.

e) Tom is musicaler than Sam.

f) Emma is the sensiblest of all the children.

g) Amy was the most skilfullest swimmer.

h) The diamond is the valuablest stone of all.

Challenger

1. Copy these sentences in your book. Underline the adverb which comes in front of the adjective in each sentence.

a) I did much better at spelling than Edward.

b) Tom can be quite funny at times.

c) Carra was the least skilful of them all.

d) The chair is very comfortable.

e) My shoes are less colourful than yours.

f) These cakes were the least expensive.

g) Mr Smith was no bigger than Mr Jones.

h) My writing is more beautiful than hers.

So – what have you learned about using adverbs with adjectives?

Focus

We can sometimes **compare adjectives**, and **put them in order**, on a **scale of intensity**.

cold ➡ **chilly** ➡ **lukewarm** ➡ **tepid** ➡ **warm** ➡ **hot**

Check it out

1 Find and write the pairs of opposite adjectives in Set A and Set B.

a)

Set A	**Set B**
high	soft
quiet	big
hard	low
small	wild
tame	noisy

b)

Set A	**Set B**
dry	empty
cold	right
smooth	hot
full	wet
wrong	rough

Practice

1. Write these adjectives in your book in order of intensity.

a) chilly   warm   cool
b) high   low   medium
c) bright   dull   shiny
d) quick   slow   supersonic
e) flexible   soft   hard
f) loudest   loud   louder
g) polite   rude   mischievous
h) smooth   prickly   lumpy

Challenger

1. Think of an adjective that could come between these opposites and write it in.

a) careless   _____   careful
b) foolish   _____   wise
c) silent   _____   noisy
d) miserable   _____   cheerful
e) calm   _____   stormy
f) dirty   _____   spotless
g) tame   _____   wild
h) obstinate   _____   docile

So – what have you learned about putting adjectives in order according to their degree of intensity?

Focus

A **phrase** is a **group of words**.

A phrase is usually **short** and does not have a **verb**.

A phrase does **not make sense on its own**.

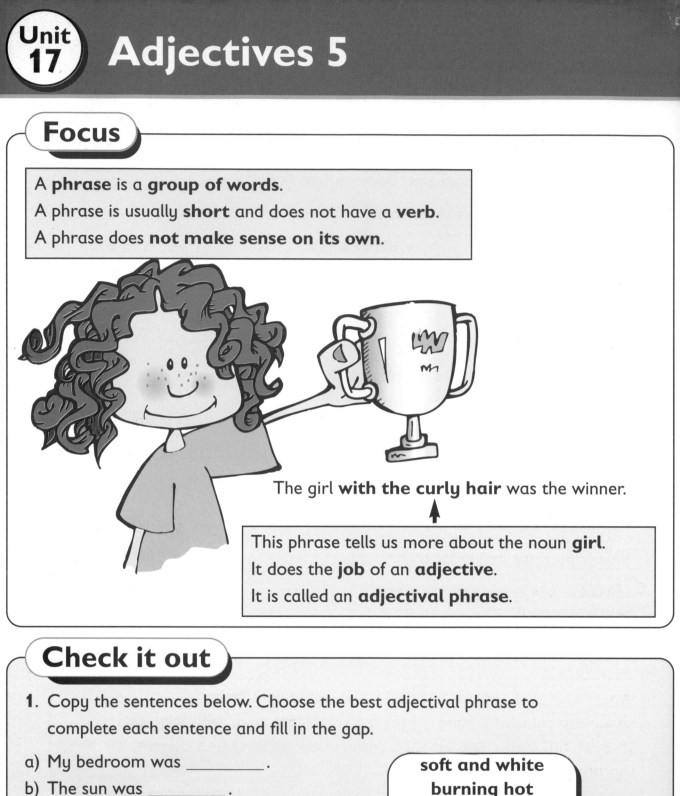

The girl **with the curly hair** was the winner.

This phrase tells us more about the noun **girl**.

It does the **job** of an **adjective**.

It is called an **adjectival phrase**.

Check it out

1. Copy the sentences below. Choose the best adjectival phrase to complete each sentence and fill in the gap.

a) My bedroom was _____ .

b) The sun was _____ .

c) The shop was _____ .

d) In the winter the street was _____ .

e) The rabbit's tail was _____ .

> **soft and white**
> **burning hot**
> **messy and dirty**
> **crowded and noisy**
> **slippery and icy**

Practice

1. Copy these sentences in your book. Choose the best adjectival phrase in the box and complete each one.

> dirty but happy   with the torn cover   neat and tidy
> rocky and snowy   dark and handsome   long and tangled
> muddy and battered   in the black anorak

a) The prince was _____ .

b) The garden was _____ .

c) The girl's hair was _____ .

d) The two children were _____ when they came home from the park.

e) My _____ car was returned to me by the police.

f) The mountain looked _____ .

g) The thief _____ came in.

h) My reading book, _____ , was found under the chair.

Challenger

1. Describe the nouns in a) to f). See how long you can make your description, without using a verb. Look at the example to see how to do it.

> the cake ➞ the chocolate cake ➞ the big chocolate cake ➞ the big chocolate cake, with icing ➞ the big chocolate cake, with icing and cherries on top ➞ the big chocolate cake, with icing and cherries on top, on a silver dish ➞ etc.

a) the car   c) the giant   e) the carpet

b) the garden   d) the monster   f) the teacher

So – what have you learned about adjectival phrases?

Focus

We sometimes **shorten** words by **missing out some letters**.
We use an **apostrophe** to show where the letters are missing.

I'm (I am) going swimming.

We're (We are) going shopping.

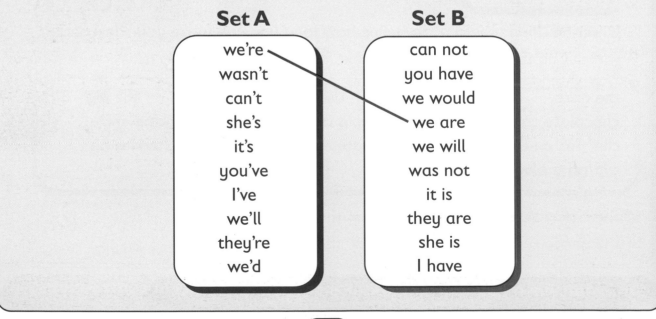

Check it out

1. Match up each contraction in Set A with its longer form in Set B.

Do it like this: **we're – we are**

Set A	Set B
we're	can not
wasn't	you have
can't	we would
she's	we are
it's	we will
you've	was not
I've	it is
we'll	they are
they're	she is
we'd	I have

Practice

1. Copy these contractions in your book. Put the missing apostrophes.

a) wasnt   f) whos   k) youve   p) itll

b) cant   g) thats   l) theyve   q) theyd

c) werent   h) hows   m) Ill   r) shes

d) shouldnt   i) theyre   n) shell   s) wed

e) theres   j) well   o) theyll   t) Ive

2. Now write what each contraction represents.

Do it like this: **wasn't – was not**

Challenger

1. Rewrite the following sentences.

Write a contraction for the underlined words.

a) We <u>can</u> <u>not</u> find our books.

b) They <u>did</u> <u>not</u> know what to do.

c) <u>He</u> <u>is</u> my best friend.

d) <u>They</u> <u>will</u> regret his actions.

e) You <u>should</u> <u>not</u> run across the road.

f) <u>I</u> <u>would</u> go if I could.

g) <u>It</u> <u>is</u> a lovely day.

h) <u>You</u> <u>are</u> my favourite friend.

i) I do not think <u>they</u> <u>will</u> be able to do it.

j) The baby <u>does</u> <u>not</u> have any shoes.

So – what have you learned about using apostrophes in contractions?

Focus

We use an **apostrophe** to **show ownership** (to show that something belongs to someone).

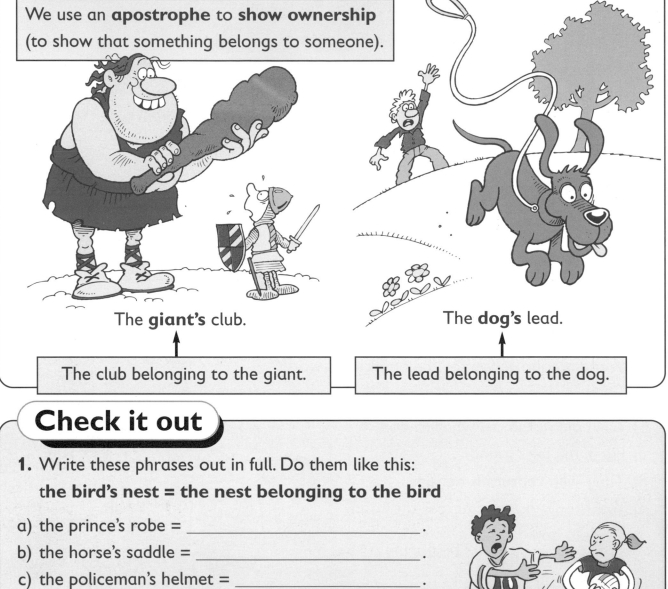

The **giant's** club.

The club belonging to the giant.

The **dog's** lead.

The lead belonging to the dog.

Check it out

1. Write these phrases out in full. Do them like this:

the bird's nest = the nest belonging to the bird

a) the prince's robe = _____.

b) the horse's saddle = _____.

c) the policeman's helmet = _____.

d) the girl's dress = _____.

e) the farmer's tractor = _____.

f) Pete's glasses = _____.

g) Amy's ball = _____.

h) Mrs Smith's shopping bag = _____.

Practice

1. Write these sentences using an apostrophe. Do them like this:

the horse belonging to the king = the king's horse

a) the ship belonging to the pirate = _____ .

b) the computer belonging to the scientist = _____ .

c) the spell belonging to the magician = _____ .

d) the banana belonging to the monkey = _____ .

e) the shorts belonging to Ali = _____ .

f) the house belonging to Mrs Shah = _____ .

g) the trunk of the elephant = _____ .

h) the hair of the cat = _____ .

Challenger

1. Rewrite these sentences. Replace the underlined words with a shorter **apostrophe + s** phrase instead. The first one has been done for you.

a) <u>The tail belonging to the dog</u> was very long.
   The dog's tail was very long.

b) <u>The car belonging to the Prime Minister</u> had an accident.

c) <u>The pen belonging to the teacher</u> got broken.

d) Robin wore <u>the cloak belonging to Batman</u>.

e) The sailors hoisted the <u>the sails of the ship</u>.

f) <u>The shirt belonging to the footballer</u> got very muddy.

g) <u>The whiskers of the cat</u> twitched.

h) <u>The puppies belonging to the dog</u> were playful.

So – what have you learned about using apostrophes to show possession?

Focus

Many **plural nouns** end in **s**. To show ownership, we put an **apostrophe** after the **s**.

If the plural noun does **not end in s**, we show ownership by adding **'s**.

The monkey**s'** tails.

The children**'s** toys.

The tails belonging to the monkeys.

The toys belonging to the children.

Check it out

1. Copy and complete these. Do them like this:

the birds' eggs = the eggs belonging to the birds

a) the boys' books = _____ .

b) the girls' teacher = _____ .

c) the builders' tools = _____ .

d) the dogs' owners = _____ .

e) the farmers' fields = _____ .

f) the trees' branches = _____ .

g) the ants' nest = _____ .

h) the pirates' ship = _____ .

Practice

1. Copy and complete these. Do them like this:

the horses belonging to the children = the children's horses

a) the cars belonging to the staff = _____ .

b) the whiskers belonging to the mice = _____ .

c) the antlers belonging to the deer = _____ .

d) the bags belonging to the women = _____ .

e) _____ = the firemen's hosepipe.

f) _____ = the children's paddling pool.

g) _____ = the fish's fins.

h) _____ = the oxen's yoke.

Challenger

1. Explain the difference between each of these.

a) the teacher's room   the teachers' room

b) the cow's calves   the cows' calves

c) the boy's shorts   the boys' shorts

d) the woman's bags   the women's bags

e) Dr Smith's car   Dr Smith's cars

f) the child's comics   the children's comics

g) the dog's ears   the dogs' ears

h) the rabbit's burrow   the rabbits' burrow

So – what have you learned about using an apostrophe to show possession with plural nouns?

Focus

The **order** in which we **place words in a sentence** can make a difference to the meaning.

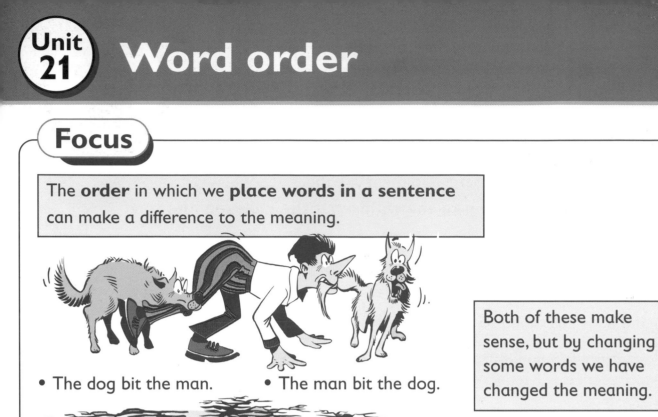

- The dog bit the man.
- The man bit the dog.

Both of these make sense, but by changing some words we have changed the meaning.

- One day a lion was sleeping in the shade under a tree.
- A lion was sleeping in the shade under a tree one day.

Sometimes we can change the order of the words in a sentence but still retain the same meaning.

Check it out

1. Rearrange the words below to make sensible sentences.

a) man   asleep.   The   fell
b) by   town   went   We   to   bus.
c) car   muddy.   My   very   got
d) carried   bag.   The   a   lady   old   heavy
e) workmen   tea.   drinking   Some   were
f) driving   farmer   a   The   tractor.   is
g) park.   The   the   played   children   in
h) I   bike   off   fell   the   in   garden.   my

Practice

1. Reorder the words in the sentences below to make some silly sentences!
   Do it like this: **The dog bit the man. The man bit the dog.**
   a) My mum fried an egg.
   b) The boy was wearing a shirt.
   c) The man flew a flag on the flagpole.
   d) The girl threw a ball and it hit a tree.

2. Rewrite each sentence. Change the verb each time to change
   the meaning of the sentences. Do it like this:
   The woman <u>washed</u> her hair. The woman <u>painted</u> her hair.

   a) The lady knitted a jumper.   c) The children read a book.
   b) The man drove his car.   d) The squirrel climbed a tree.

Challenger

1. Experiment with the word order in these sentences. Rearrange some of the
   words but try to keep the same meaning. (You can change the punctuation or
   add another word or two if you wish.) Have another look at the example in
   the 'Focus' box opposite before you begin.

   a) One day a lion was sleeping in the shade under a tree.
   b) A little mouse ran over the lion's paw and woke him up.
   c) When he woke up the lion roared with laughter.
   d) Some days later the lion got caught in a hunter's net.
   e) Try as he might, the lion could not free himself.

**So – what have you learned about the
importance of word order in sentences?**

Focus

Simon was feeling tired**.** He went home.

> The **two sentences** are separated by a **full stop**.

Simon was feeling tired **so** he went home.

> The two sentences are **connected** with a **conjunction** (the joining word **so**).

As he was feeling tired**,** Simon went home.

> The **word order** has been **changed** and a **new word** (**as**) has been **added**.
> A **comma** has been used to join the sentence together.

Check it out

1. Make the pairs of sentences below into one sentence. Choose the best conjunction to help you.

a) The lady put up her umbrella. It was raining. (because, and, but)

b) I tried hard. I could not do it. (and, so, but)

c) The man sat down. He watched television. (if, and, when)

d) I hurt my leg. I was playing football. (after, and, when)

e) The car is useless. It is broken. (but, while, because)

f) I asked John to come. He refused. (and, so, but)

g) Mrs Jones will go shopping. It does not rain. (if, so, because)

h) Tom waved to Sam. She did not see him. (and, when, but)

Practice

1. Rewrite each sentence below as two shorter sentences.

a) Jack could not lift the box because it was too heavy.

b) I went to the window and looked out.

c) As it was late, Edward went to bed.

d) When Tom told a lie, the teacher was angry.

e) This is the girl who lost her bag.

f) We walked across the road which ran through town.

g) It rained heavily so I got soaked.

h) I read my book while Emma watched television.

Challenger

1. Copy the sentences below. Put in the missing commas.

a) After the police captured the thief they handcuffed him.

b) Because he was ill Tom could not go out.

c) While she was singing Amy baked a cake.

d) Tom wondering what to do walked along the road.

e) As I waited for the bus I whistled to myself.

f) The rabbit which was only young came out of the burrow.

g) Although the sky was cloudy we could still see the moon.

h) Mr Barnes who is my next door neighbour threw my ball back.

2. Now rewrite each of the sentences as two shorter sentences.

So – what have you learned about joining sentences?

Focus

We can **change** different **classes of words** in different ways by using different **suffixes**. The **way** a word **is suffixed** often tells us what **class of word** it is, (for example: a noun, a verb or an adjective).

The green toad hopped along.

We can suffix many **verbs** by adding **ed** in the **past tense**.

The green toaded hop along.

We **can't** add the **ed** suffix to **nouns**. It looks wrong!

The greened toad hop along.

We **can't** add the **ed** to **adjectives**. It looks wrong!

Check it out

1. Two common ways of suffixing verbs are by adding **ing** or **ed**. Copy and complete this table. Take care with the spelling!

Root verb	Verb + 'ing'	Verb + 'ed'
laugh	laughing	laughed
wash	washing	
dream		dreamed
	resting	
smile		
		cried
hurry		
	grabbing	
drum		
skated		

Practice

1. Copy each sentence below and underline the verb. Then rewrite each sentence using the **ing** and **ed** form of the verb.
   The first one has been done for you.

a) Julius Caesar <u>invades</u> Britain. **Julius Caesar was <u>invading</u> Britain.**
   Julius Caesar <u>invaded</u> Britain.

b) Paul copies Emma's address.

c) The alligator snaps its jaws.

d) Mr Patel walks quickly.

e) Edward snores loudly.

f) The knight defends the castle.

g) The children behave well.

h) Ben and Miguel try hard at school.

Challenger

1. The wrong word has been suffixed in each sentence. Rewrite each sentence, suffixing the verb correctly. Be careful with your spelling!

a) I am carry a basketing.

b) Emma hug hered Mum.

c) The childing was run for the bus.

d) The teachered look out of the window.

e) I like eat a sweeting.

f) Ben hurry home aftered school.

g) The crowd applaud the footballed team.

h) As I was go to school, I saw a huging crocodile.

So – what have you learned about what we can gain by looking at the way words are suffixed, e.g. verbs?

Focus

We can **change** different **classes of words** in different ways by using different **suffixes**. The **way** a word **is suffixed** often tells us what **class of word** it is, for example: a noun, a verb or an adjective.

The wet girls ran home.

The wets girl ran home.

We can suffix many nouns by adding **s** or **es** in the plural.

We can't add the **s** suffix to adjectives. It looks wrong!

Check it out

1. Copy these tables and fill in the missing words.

a)

Singular	Plural
table	tables
chair	
fox	
bush	
potato	
tomato	

b)

Singular	Plural
pot	pots
	forks
	churches
	glasses
	volcanoes
	echoes

Practice

1. Copy these tables and fill in the missing words.

   Take care with the spelling!

a)

Singular	Plural
city	cities
lady	
baby	
copy	
leaf	
shelf	
wolf	
calf	

b)

Singular	Plural
fairy	fairies
	pennies
	lies
	lorries
	halves
	thieves
	loaves
	wives

Challenger

1. The wrong word has been suffixed in each sentence below. Rewrite each sentence again, suffixing the noun correctly. Be careful with your spelling!

a) We saw lots of lovelys church.

b) I listened to the louds echo.

c) The wilds fox were hungry.

d) The loaf were crustys.

e) Some huges lorry thundered along.

f) The cruels thief were caught.

g) The reddests apple are the best.

h) The girl were the fastests.

So – what have you learned about what we can gain by looking at the way words are suffixed, e.g. nouns?

Focus

We use **speech marks** when we write down what people say.
Only the words that are actually spoken go inside the speech marks.

"What's the problem?" the mechanic asked.

The man replied, "The engine won't start."

Check it out

1. Rewrite these sentences. Put in the missing speech marks.

a) Edward said, It must be my turn next.

b) I like reading best of all, said Shahidi.

c) Asif said, There is a new clothes shop in town.

d) My favourite team is Liverpool, Kim said.

e) Mrs Merton shouted, I hate sprouts!

f) Have you ever stayed up after midnight? James asked.

g) It's not fair! Nasi moaned.

h) My painting is better than yours, Raza jeered.

2. Now underline the actual words each person said in each
sentence you have written.

Practice

1. Rewrite the sentences in your book. Put in the missing punctuation marks.

a) please will you read me a story sam asked

b) the lady said the red dress is the smartest

c) stop that at once shouted the angry motorist

d) it costs three pounds the assistant explained

e) i cant find my shoes the boy cried

f) where do you think you are going the policeman enquired

g) im dying for a drink leo groaned

h) i would like to see what new books you have the man requested

Challenger

1. Write this short play in sentence form, using speech marks.

   Do it like this: **Shireen: I'm hungry – Shireen said, "I'm hungry."**

Shireen:	I'm hungry.
Her mum:	What would you like to eat?
Shireen:	I would like some chocolate.
Her mum:	If you eat sweets now you won't eat your dinner.
Shireen:	I'll starve if I don't eat something soon!
Her mum:	Don't be so silly!
Shireen:	What can I have, then?
Her mum:	How about a nice piece of fruit?
Shireen:	Yes. That will do. I'll have an apple.

2. Make up a conversation between Shireen and her mum, when Shireen asks to stay up late to watch the television. Write it down as a continuation of the play above.

So – what have you learned about using speech marks?

Focus

Hyphens and **dashes** both look the same (although dashes are usually longer) – but they do **different jobs**.

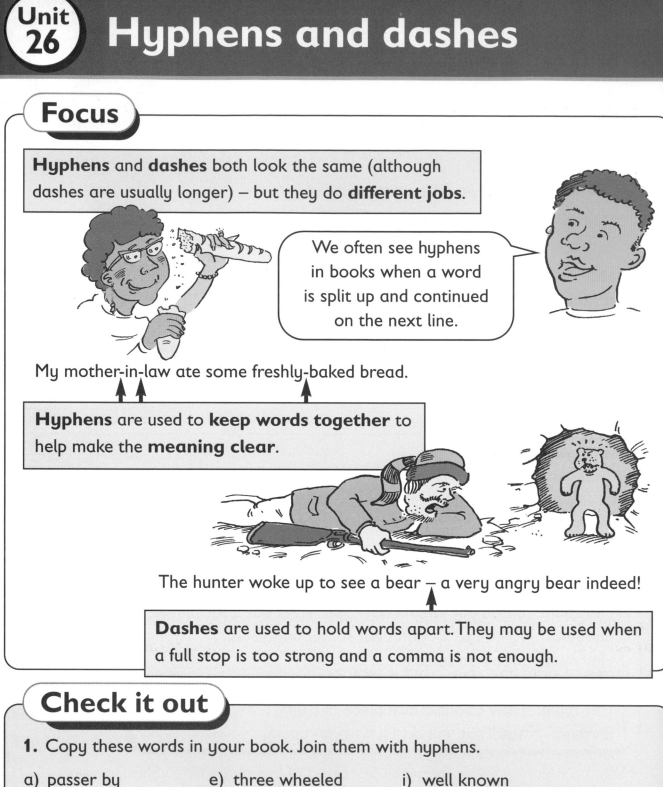

We often see hyphens in books when a word is split up and continued on the next line.

My mother-in-law ate some freshly-baked bread.

Hyphens are used to **keep words together** to help make the **meaning clear**.

The hunter woke up to see a bear – a very angry bear indeed!

Dashes are used to hold words apart. They may be used when a full stop is too strong and a comma is not enough.

Check it out

1. Copy these words in your book. Join them with hyphens.

a) passer by

b) son in law

c) hanger on

d) step daughter

e) three wheeled

f) sure footed

g) light fingered

h) lift off

i) well known

j) double edged

k) clean shaven

l) bald headed

Practice

1. Copy these sentences in your book. Put in the missing dashes.

a) James dyed his hair pink but now he has dyed it green!

b) John Smith is a famous guitarist one of the best.

c) Lady Burns had many trees in her garden willows, elms and oak trees.

d) I want to leave at noon so make sure you are ready.

e) There is only one person who can do it me!

f) The dog a hairy beast jumped up at me.

g) Try to watch the programme if you have time it's wonderful.

h) Wow you look marvellous!

Challenger

1. Copy these sentences. Circle each hyphen and dash. Above each write if it is a hyphen (H) or a dash (D) that is being used. The first one has been done for you.

a) There it was at last **(D)** — Treasure Island.

b) The lady was an animal-lover.

c) My brother is football-mad.

d) Animals – like sheep, cows and horses – may all be found on farms.

e) I tried to drink the soup – but it was too hot.

f) The old-looking man was in rags.

g) The long-legged giraffe ran off.

h) The frog – who was really a prince – croaked at the princess.

2. Find and copy five examples of hyphens and five examples of dashes used in books.

So – what have you learned about hyphens and dashes?

Focus

This is a **colon :** A colon is used in **two ways** in books.

It may be used to **introduce a list**.

It is sometimes used to **introduce direct speech** (before someone speaks).

You will need: scissors, paper and pencils.

The girl remembered the ghost's warning: "Don't look back!"

This is a **semi-colon ;** A semi-colon is used in **two ways** in books.

It can **balance two parts of a sentence.**

It can **break up lists**, like a comma.

The guide opened the door; he showed us into our room.

Before the picnic we packed everything including a box for the plates and cutlery; cartons of sandwiches; bottles of drink; and a tablecloth and serviettes.

Check it out

1. Copy these sentences. Underline the colons and circle the semi-colons.

a) The ingredients are: eggs, butter, flour and milk.

b) On the table stood plates of meat; dishes of salads; bowls of fruit and drinks.

c) On the board it said: "No skating allowed."

d) I'm pleased to see you; come in and explain why you are late.

e) Here is the team: Holden, Carey, Giles and Paul.

f) This was the message: "Take care."

Practice

1. Copy the sentences below. Put in the missing colons.

a) The note on the table said "I'll be back at teatime."

b) In the comic there were cartoons, stories and games.

c) I could hear a voice shouting "Get out of here!"

d) Here are the winning numbers 64, 72, 8 and 12.

e) We will pass these towns Dover, Folkestone and Hythe.

f) The voice came from the attic "Help! I'm stuck!"

g) Inside the card someone had written 'With best wishes'.

h) I want to see these children Tom, Sally, Sam and Raza.

Challenger

1. Copy the sentences below. Put in the missing semi-colons.

a) From the top we could see a winding river a little village a dark wood and a small church.

b) It was too noisy for her she decided she would have to move.

c) The heavens opened it began to rain heavily.

d) The boat had a hole in its bows it sank slowly into the water.

e) Lots of smells drifted on the air such as cakes being baked bonfires burning grass cuttings and strong car fumes.

2. Find and copy five examples of colons and five examples of semi-colons used in books.

So – what have you learned about colons and semi-colons?

Focus

There are **four main types of sentence**.

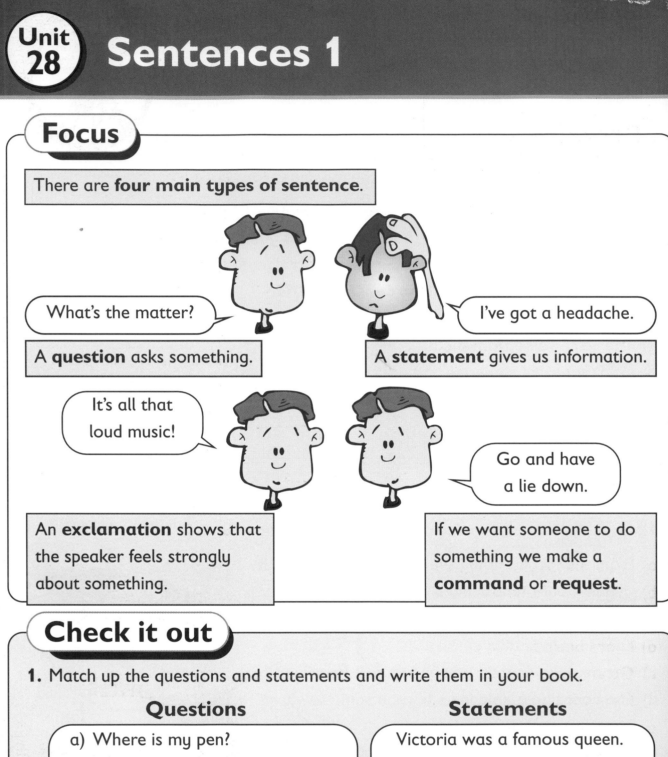

What's the matter?

I've got a headache.

A **question** asks something.

A **statement** gives us information.

It's all that loud music!

Go and have a lie down.

An **exclamation** shows that the speaker feels strongly about something.

If we want someone to do something we make a **command** or **request**.

Check it out

1. Match up the questions and statements and write them in your book.

Questions	Statements
a) Where is my pen?	Victoria was a famous queen.
b) What is the capital of France?	I hit a ball through the glass.
c) Who was Victoria?	Your pen is on the table.
d) When is Christmas?	I am going swimming.
e) How did you break the window?	Christmas is in December.
f) Why are you carrying a towel?	Paris is the capital of France.

Practice

1. These commands are in the wrong order. Rewrite them correctly.

- Get in the bath.
- Get out of the bath.
- Dry yourself on a towel.
- Take off your clothes.
- Put in the plug.
- Get dressed.
- Fill the bath with warm water.
- Have a thorough wash.

Challenger

1. Copy these sentences. After each, write if it is a statement (S),
a question (Q), a command (C) or an exclamation (E).

a) What happened to my sweets?

b) What a nightmare!

c) Look at the state you're in!

d) I have been playing in the park.

e) Go and have a wash.

f) It's not fair!

g) How can you get so muddy?

h) It's really lovely!

2. Find and copy five examples of commands and
five examples of exclamations used in books.

So – what have you learned about different types of sentences?

Focus

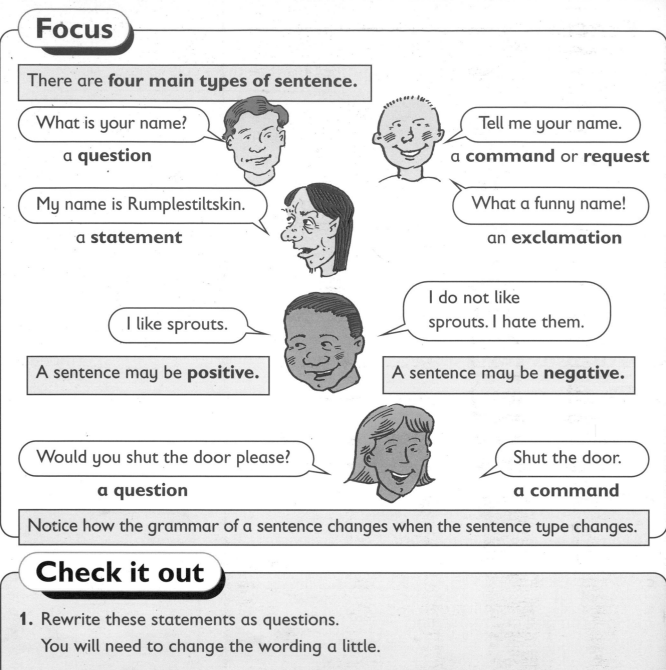

There are **four main types of sentence.**

What is your name?

a **question**

Tell me your name.

a **command** or **request**

My name is Rumplestiltskin.

a **statement**

What a funny name!

an **exclamation**

I like sprouts.

I do not like sprouts. I hate them.

A sentence may be **positive.**

A sentence may be **negative.**

Would you shut the door please?

a question

Shut the door.

a command

Notice how the grammar of a sentence changes when the sentence type changes.

Check it out

1. Rewrite these statements as questions.
You will need to change the wording a little.

a) Emma got her spellings right.

b) It is nearly teatime.

c) Dogs bark a lot.

d) Horses neigh.

e) The farmer ploughed his field in the autumn.

f) The rocket ship blasted off into space.

g) My favourite meal is curry and rice.

h) A computer has a brain like a human being.

Practice

1. Rewrite these positive statements as negative ones.

a) The sea is calm.

b) Tom likes art and science.

c) The team won the match easily.

d) The mountaineers soon reached the summit.

2. Rewrite these negative statements as positive ones.

a) I do not like coffee.

b) I could not do my homework.

c) Tom was unable to buy the toy.

d) It stopped raining after lunch.

Challenger

1. Rewrite each of these questions as an order. For example:

Can you see Edward? might be written as **Look for Edward**.

a) Could you finish your apple please?

b) Can you do it?

c) May I go to the toilet?

d) What time is it?

e) Why are you laughing at me?

f) Would you pass me the salt?

g) Shall I turn off the light?

h) Will you come out to play with me?

So – what have you learned about the way the grammar of a sentence alters when we alter the sentence type?

Focus

When we put forward an **argument**, we try and **persuade** someone to our **point of view**.

There are many **words** we can use which **help us to explain clearly** what we think.

> **I think** sport is good for you **because** it helps keep you fit. If you do not get enough exercise **then** you become unhealthy. **Therefore,** everyone should turn off their computers and go for a good walk!

Check it out

1. Here are some helpful words to learn.

> firstly   secondly   finally   surely   next   different   although
> because   besides   however   furthermore   moreover

a) List the words that end in **ly** in your book.

b) List the words that begin with **be**.

c) List the words in alphabetical order.

2.

> next   different   although   however   furthermore   moreover

a) List the shortest and longest words in the set above.

b) List the word with seven letters.

c) List the words with eight letters.

d) List the word with nine letters.

Practice

1. Rewrite this passage. Choose the best word to fill each gap.

I (believe, think) that everyone should have a pet (because, since) they teach you how to look after things. (Next, Secondly) pets are like people – they become part of your family and make good friends. (On the other hand, But) they can take up a lot of time. (Also, And) they can cost a lot of money. (However, Finally) I do think pets are good for you – (but, so) you do need to think carefully before you get one!

Challenger

1. Make up an argument for more pocket money.
Use the outline below to help you to write your own.

I think I should have more pocket money because_____.

Secondly _____.

Furthermore _____.

On the other hand, some people might argue that _____.

However, I believe I have shown _____.

So – what have you learned about helpful words to use when arguing a case?

Range of Books Available

Year 3 Sentence	Year 4 Sentence	Year 5 Sentence	Year 6 Sentence
Year 3 Word	Year 4 Word	Year 5 Word	Year 6 Word

Literacy Differentiation Sentence Level Year 4

First published 1999
Reprinted 1999

Letts Educational,
9–15 Aldine Street, London W12 8AW
Tel: 020 8740 2270   Fax: 202 8740 2280

Text © Louis Fidge and Ray Barker

Illustrations © Richard Duszczak, David Lock, Tim Oliver, John Plumb, Sylvie Poggio Artists Agency (Simon Jacobs) and Ken Vail Graphic Design (Liz Bryan)

Designed by Ken Vail Graphic Design, Cambridge

British Library Cataloguing-in-Publication Data
A CIP record for this book is available from the British Library

ISBN: 1 84085 234 8

Printed in the UK by Bath Press Limited

Every effort has been made to trace copyright holders and to obtain their permission for the use of copyright material. The authors and publishers would gladly receive information enabling them to rectify an error or omission in subsequent editions.

Letts Educational is the trading name of BPP [Letts Educational] Ltd